NEIL A. KJOS
PIANO LIBRARY

MW00378449

LEVEL FIVE

ESSENTIAL PIANO REPERTOIRE

From the 17th, 18th, & 19th Centuries

SELECTED & EDITED BY

Keith Snell

10075 SW Beaverton-Hillsdale Hwy.
Beaverton, Oregon 97005
(503) 641-5691 (800) 876-9777
Fax: (503) 643-7527
ISBN 0-8497-6355-X

THE NEIL A. KJOS PIANO LIBRARY

The **Neil A. Kjos Piano Library** is a comprehensive series of piano music in a wide variety of musical styles. The library is divided into eleven levels and will provide students with a complete performance experience in both solo and ensemble music. Teachers will find the carefully graded levels appropriate when choosing repertoire for evaluations, auditions, festivals, and examinations. Included in the **Neil A. Kjos Piano Library:**

Preparatory Level – Level Ten

Fundamentals of Piano Theory
Piano Repertoire: Baroque & Classical
Piano Repertoire: Romantic & 20th Century
Piano Repertoire: Etudes
Scale Skills
Essential Piano Repertoire
Music of the 21st Century
New Age Piano
Jazz Piano
One Piano Four Hands
Music for Christmas

PREFACE

Essential Piano Repertoire from the **Neil A. Kjos Piano Library** provides piano students with carefully chosen collections of the very best keyboard literature from the 17th, 18th, and 19th Centuries. The appropriately graded levels ensure steady and thorough progress as pianists advance in their study of the baroque, classical, and romantic styles.

Compact disc recordings, performed by pianist Diane Hidy, are included in each volume of *Essential Piano Repertoire*. The interpretations follow the editions closely as practical examples for students.

Contents

GP455

Courante

Track
1

George Frideric Handel
(1685-1759)

Allegro

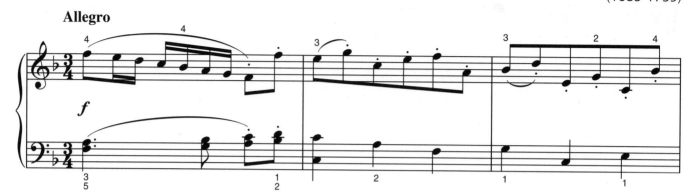

Prelude

BWV 927
From Eighteen Little Preludes

Track 2

Johann Sebastian Bach
(1685-1750)

Prelude
BWV 846

Track 3

Johann Sebastian Bach
(1685-1750)

8

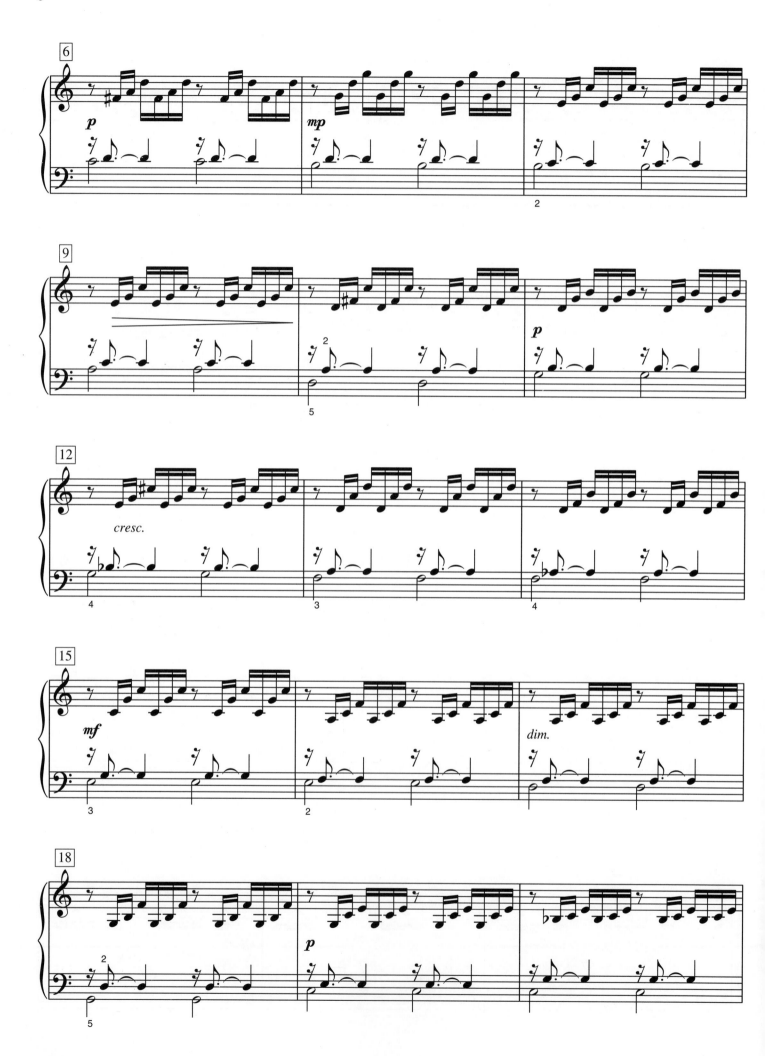

GP455

Solfeggietto

Track 4

Carl Philipp Emanuel Bach
(1714-1788)

Sonatina

Track
5

George Benda
(1722-1795)

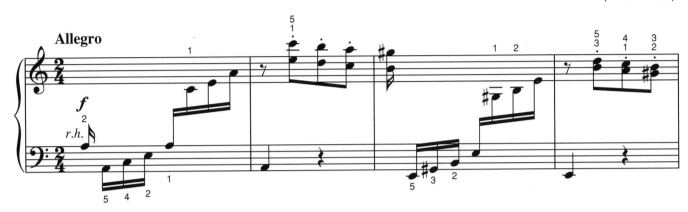

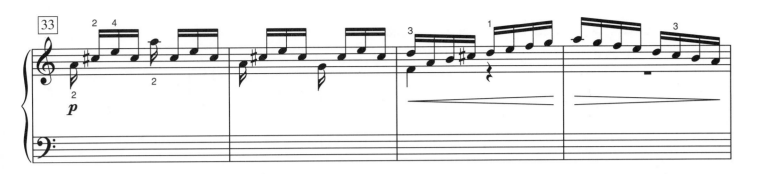

D.C. al Fine

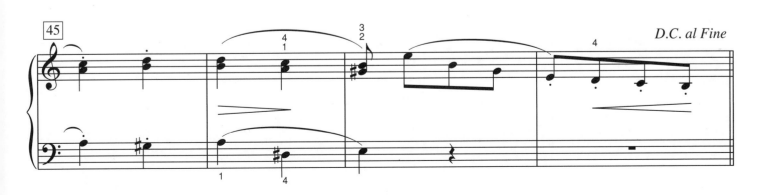

Allegro Scherzando

Joseph Haydn
(1732-1809)

Sonatina

Op. 36, No. 3

I.

Muzio Clementi
(1752-1832)

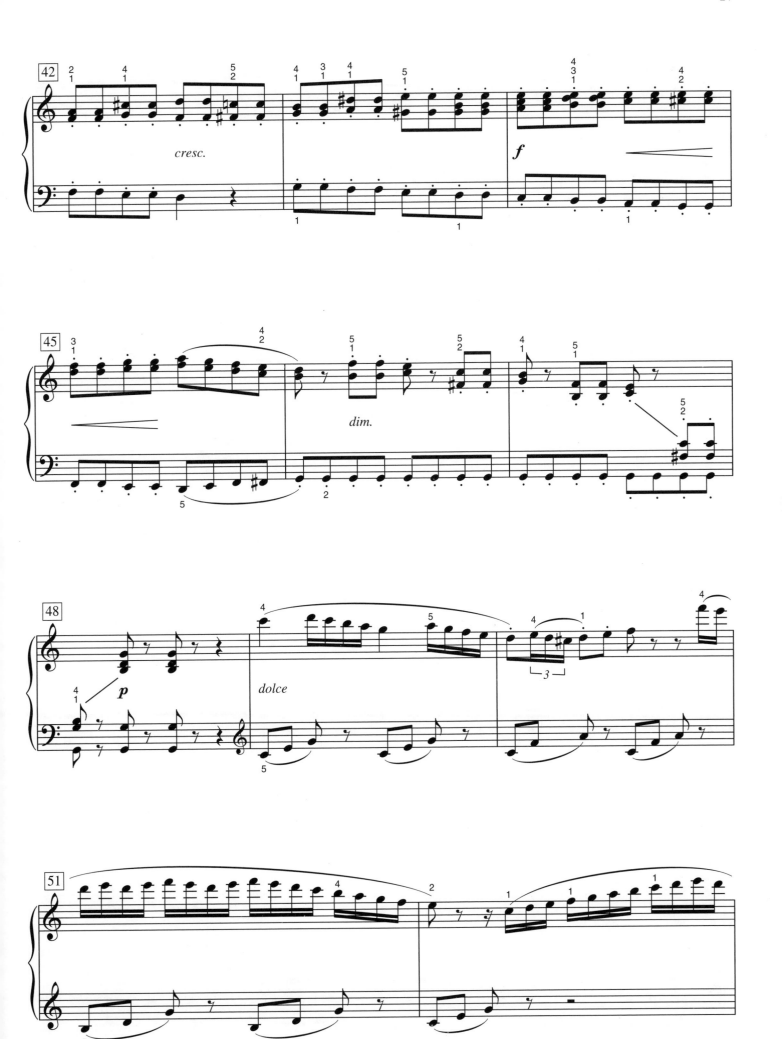

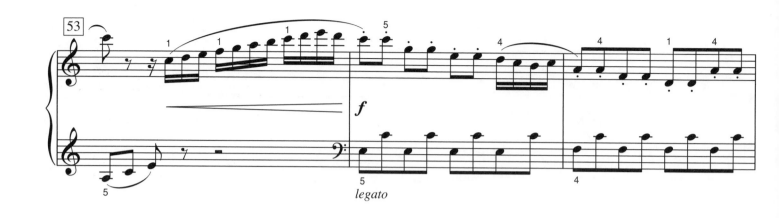

II.

Un poco adagio

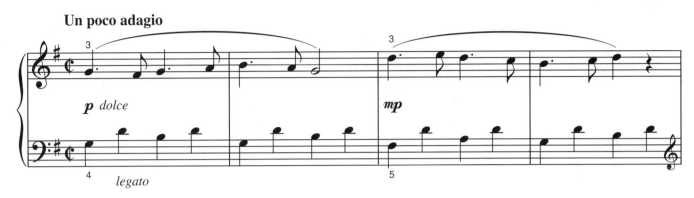

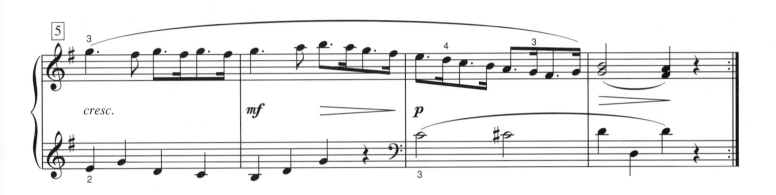

III.

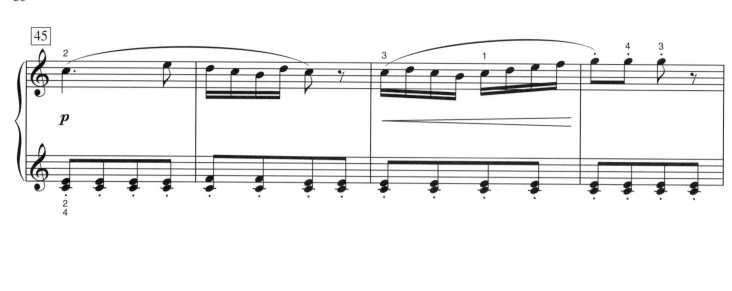

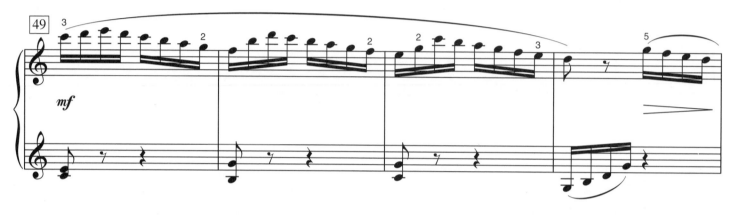

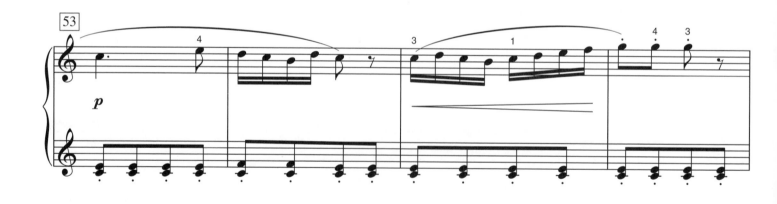

Sonatina
Op. 55, No. 3

I.

Friedrich Kuhlau
(1786-1832)

II.

Allegretto grazioso

GP455

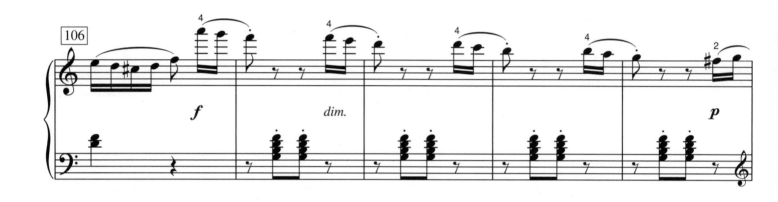

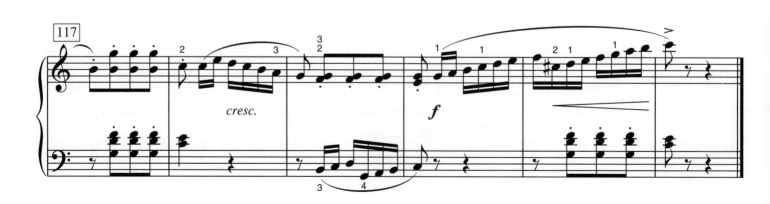

For Elise

Ludwig van Beethoven
(1770-1827)

Harmony of the Angels

Op. 100, No. 21

Friedrich Burgmüller
(1806-1874)

Knight Ruppert

Op. 68, No. 12

Robert Schumann
(1810-1856)

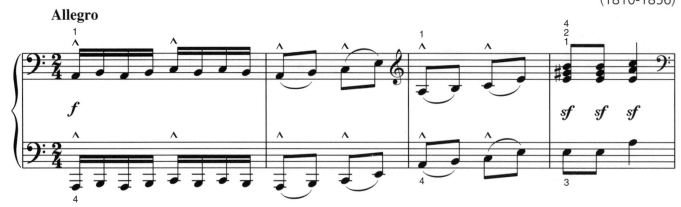

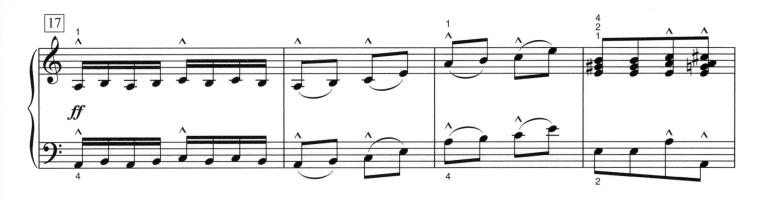

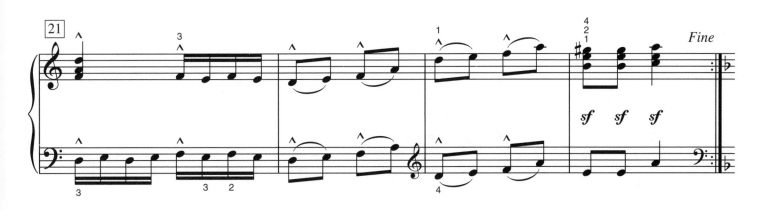

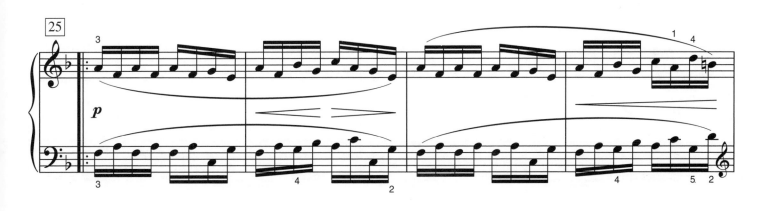

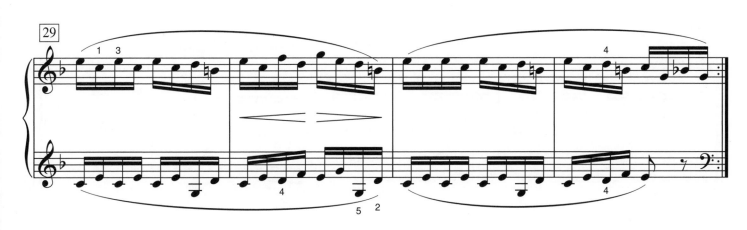

D.C. senza repetizione al Fine

Prelude
Op. 28, No. 7

Track
15

Frédéric Chopin
(1810-1849)

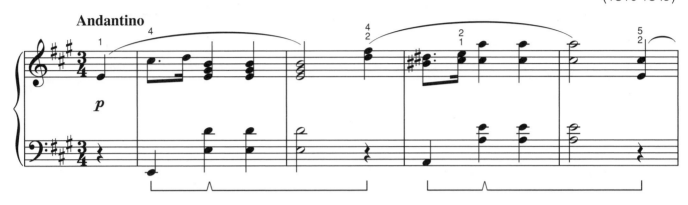

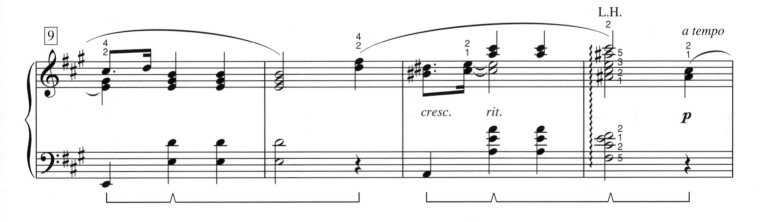

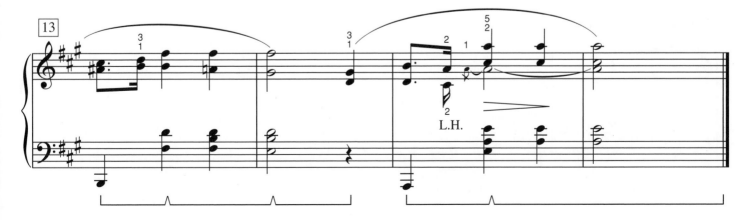

Avalanche

Track
16

Stephen Heller
(1814-1888)

The Orphan

Op. 64, No. 4

Louis Streabbog
(1835-1886)

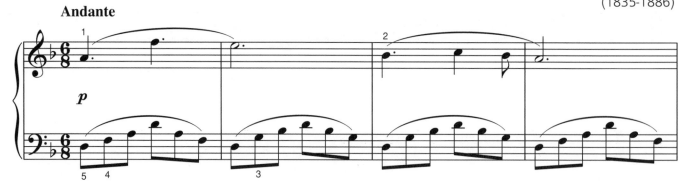

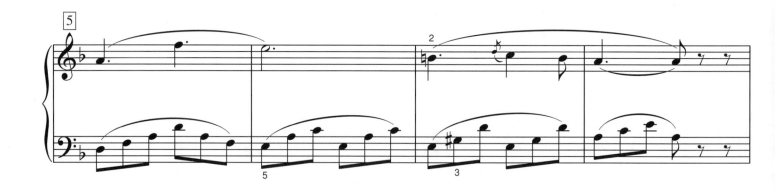

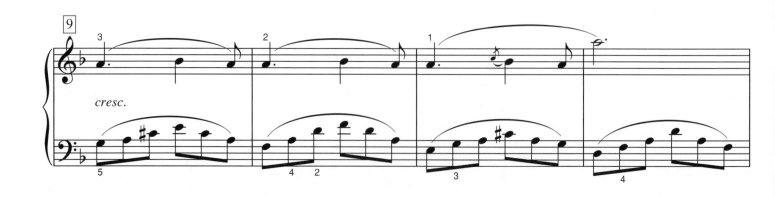

Grandmother's Minuet

Op. 68, No. 2

Edvard Grieg
(1843-1907)

Allegretto grazioso e leggierissimo

poco rit.

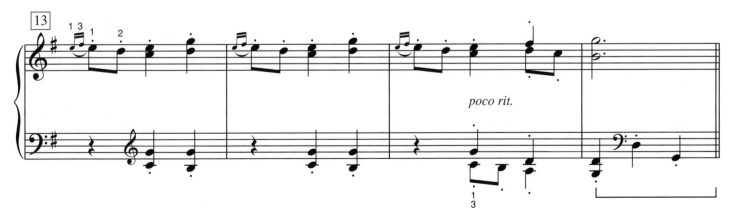

54

GP455

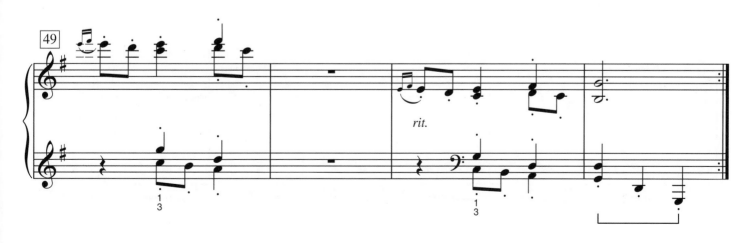

Italian Song

Op. 39, No. 15

Peter Ilyich Tchaikovsky
(1840-1893)

Track
19

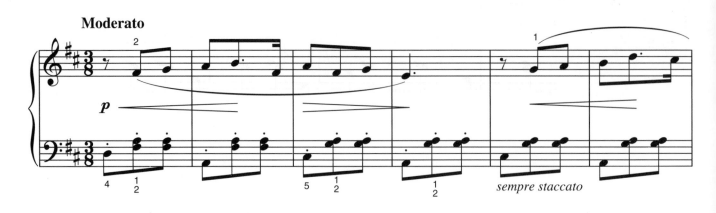

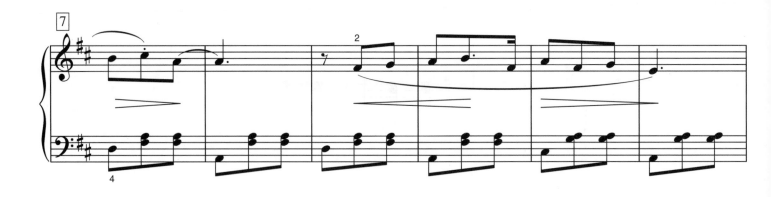

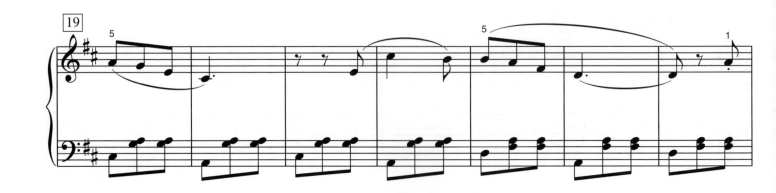

Waltz

Track
20

Vladimir Rebikov
(1866-1920)

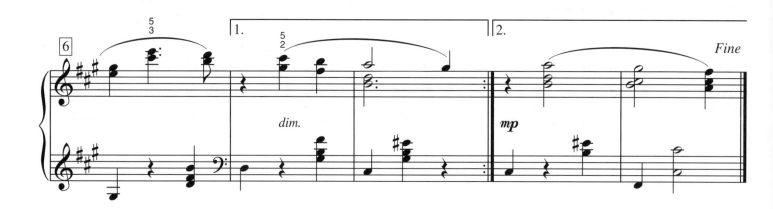

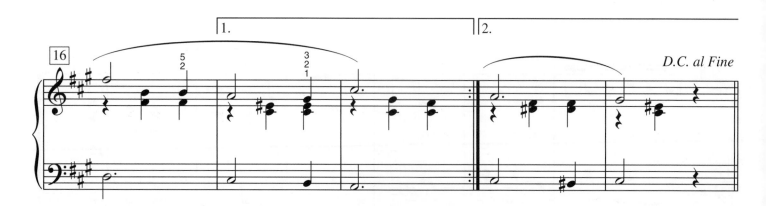

Le Petit Noir

Claude Debussy
(1862-1918)

COMPOSER BIOGRAPHIES

Carl Philipp Emanuel Bach (1714 – 1788) was a German composer and the second son of J.S. Bach. Widely acclaimed throughout Europe, he was the leading court musician of Frederick the Great in Berlin. His pre-classical style was important during the transition from the Baroque period into the Classical period. His keyboard works influenced composers such as Haydn, Mozart, and Beethoven. His essay *True Art of Keyboard Playing* is one of the first important piano methods, and a definitive source on the style and performance practices of his time.

Johann Sebastian Bach (1685 – 1750) was a German composer, regarded as the greatest composer of the Baroque period. He had numerous relatives who were musicians: from seven generations, 193 out of 200 were musicians. Throughout his life, he held positions at various churches and in royal courts, and for almost thirty years he was the director of music at the St. Thomas School in Leipzig. He was married twice and had twenty children, several of whom became well known musicians. Bach was a prolific composer; his complete works fill forty-six large volumes containing choral music, concertos, orchestral and chamber works, and organ and clavier (keyboard) music.

Ludwig van Beethoven (1770 – 1827) was a German composer and pianist. Beethoven's father insisted that Beethoven practice long hours in hopes he would become a child prodigy like Mozart. In 1787 he visited Vienna, where he played for Mozart, who predicted an outstanding musical career for Beethoven. In 1792 he studied with Haydn for about a year. About this time, Beethoven began to earn his living from the sale of compositions and from teaching. He became an honored and respected musician to many royal families. In his early thirties, Beethoven experiences hearing loss which later resulted in total deafness. A prolific composer, Beethoven wrote thirty-two piano sonatas, five piano concertos, one violin concerto, nine symphonies, an opera, a great quantity of chamber music, and many other works.

George Benda (1722 – 1795), an important Bohemian composer, studied in Jicin before moving to Prussia. There, he was appointed Kapellmeister to Duke Friedrich III of Saxe-Gotha. He traveled to Vienna and Hamburg before finally settling in Kostritz. Benda's compositions are distinguished by their dramatic use of alternating moods. This became characteristic of the North German style of composition, and influenced the development of opera in Germany.

Friedrich Burgmüller (1806 – 1874), German composer, came from a musical family. He moved to Paris in 1832, where he enjoyed a considerable reputation as a pianist, composer, and piano teacher. Burgmuller is particularly noted for his three sets of etudes for piano: Op. 100, Op. 105, and Op. 109.

Frédéric Chopin (1810 – 1849), born in Poland, lived most of his life in Paris, France. He was a child prodigy at the piano (some say that his talent rivaled that of Mozart). By the time he was twenty, he had already written fifty works for the piano. Chopin was dedicated to writing music for the piano and rarely composed for any other instrument. He wrote over two hundred works for the piano during his lifetime. His piano music is often regarded as the most thoroughly pianistic music ever written.

Muzio Clementi (1752 – 1832) was a famous Italian pianist, composer, and teacher. In 1781, he and Mozart had a contest to determine which one was the better pianist. Although no winner was announced, Clementi was thought to have a better technique, but the audience felt that Mozart was a better musician. Clementi wrote *The Art of Playing on the Piano-Forte*, a method which he used with his beginning students. Chopin also used this book with his students. In addition to his teaching, composing, and performing, Clementi established a successful piano factory and a publishing company.

Claude Debussy (1862 – 1918), French composer and pianist, is regarded as the creator of the Impressionist period in music. Influenced by many non-western musical styles, Debussy introduced a style of composition which included the use of Oriental pentatonic scales, the whole-tone scale, consecutive parallel chords and intervals, unresolved harmonies, and the abandonment of traditional form. He was also influenced by the sound of American Jazz, which is evident in *Le Petit Noir* and *Golliwogg's Cakewalk.* His large output of piano music includes two books of preludes, two books of etudes, and many suites, including *Estampes, Images, Suite Bergmasque* (which includes the famous *Clair de Lune*), and *Pour le Piano.* He also wrote songs, instrumental music, and many works for orchestra.

Edvard Grieg (1843 – 1907), born in Bergen, Norway, was a famous pianist and composer during his lifetime. His writing style is unique for its use of Norwegian folksong. His most frequently performed works are the *Lyric Pieces for Piano*, and the *Piano Concerto in A Minor*. Grieg also wrote many works for orchestra, including the suite *Peer Gynt*.

George Frideric Handel (1685 – 1759) was born in Halle, Germany, which was then the kingdom of Saxony. He was the son of a barber-surgeon who looked unkindly on music as a profession. To appease his father, Handel studied law briefly while earning his livelihood as a church organist. Although he wrote forty operas, he became most famous for his oratorios, of which the best known, the *Messiah*, was written in twenty-four days! He founded the Royal Academy of Music in London. In addition to vocal music, Handel wrote instrumental, organ, and keyboard music.

Joseph Haydn (1732 – 1809) An Austrian composer, who as a youth studied singing, violin, and clavier, and became a choirboy to the Vienna Cathedral. He spent more than thirty years in the service of Prince Esterhazy, a Hungarian nobleman, at Eisenstadt. Haydn was a major influence in the development of the symphony, sonata, and string quartet. During his long life, he composed approximately eighty-three string quartets, more than fifty piano sonatas, two hundred songs, one hundred and four symphonies, eighteen operas, a vast amount of church music, concertos, and many other works.

Stephen Heller (1814 – 1888), a Hungarian pianist and composer, showed such extraordinary ability as a youth that he was sent to study piano in Vienna with Czerny. He toured in Austria, Germany, England, and eventually settled in Paris, where he lived for the rest of his life. He became a very successful pianist and was friends with Chopin and Liszt. He wrote hundreds of piano pieces which became very popular and included salon dances, character pieces, and studies.

Friedrich Kuhlau (1786 – 1832) was born in Hamurg, Germany, where he was highly regarded as a pianist, piano teacher, and composer. In 1810, he moved to Copenhagen, Denmark. There he became known as the Great Danish Composer when he composed several successful operas which used popular national songs. In 1825, Kuhlau gained the respect and friendship of Ludwig van Beethoven during a visit to Vienna. It was on this occasion that Beethoven wrote a humorous canon on Kuhlau's name: Kuhl, nicht lau – cool, not lukewarm! Today, Kuhlau is best known for his sonatas and sonatinas for the piano and his many works for the flute.

Vladimir Rebikov (1866 – 1920), a Russian composer, studied at the Moscow Conservatory. His many piano pieces were influenced by French Impressionism as evident in his use of the whole-tone scale and the abandonment of traditional form. A melodious waltz from his children's opera *The Christmas Tree* is his most popular composition. He published numerous articles on music and wrote some of the finest works for young pianists.

Robert Schumann (1810 – 1856) German composer and pianist, who wrote his first piano pieces when he was seven. In 1832, Schumann injured his hand and began to devote his energies to composition rather than playing the piano. In 1840, he married Clara Wieck, a brilliant pianist who performed many of Schumann's works. Schumann wrote about other musicians as a critic in his magazine, *The New Music Journal*; he was the first to report on the importance of Chopin and Brahms. In 1850, Schumann was appointed Musical Director for the city of Dusseldorf. He held that position until 1853 when mental illness compelled him to resign. His compositions include symphonies, many piano works, a piano concerto, chamber music, songs, and choral works.

Louis Streabbog (1835 – 1886) was a French pianist, composer, and teacher. He wrote hundreds of piano pieces, many of which were for his students. His last name was actually Gobbaerts, but he preferred to publish his music under the name Streabbog: Gobbaerts spelled backwards.

Peter Ilyich Tchaikovsky (1840 – 1893), a Russian composer, studied with Anton Rubinstein at the Moscow Conservatory. Tchaikovsy became a professor of harmony at the Conservatory when he was twenty-six. He was supported through financial difficulties by Madame von Meck, a wealthy widow whom he never met. The security of the stipend he received from her enabled him to compose a great quantity of music. He traveled to America in 1891, where he was well received as a composer. His works include the ballets *Swan Lake, The Sleeping Beauty,* and *The Nutcracker*; the *Piano Concerto in B-flat Minor*; many orchestral works, choral music, chamber music, songs, and piano music.